CHRISTMAS SING-ALONG CAR·I·OKE

David Schiller

Workman Publishing • N

CONTENTS

We Wish You a Merry Christmas TRACK 1

First verse:
We wish you a merry Christmas,
We wish you a merry Christmas,
We wish you a merry Christmas,
And a happy New Year!

Repeat first verse

Bridge:
Glad tidings we bring
To you and your kin;
Glad tidings for Christmas
And a happy New Year!

Second verse:
Now bring us some figgy pudding,
Now bring us some figgy pudding,
Now bring us some figgy pudding,
And a cup of good cheer!

Third verse:
We won't go until we get some,
We won't go until we get some,
We won't go until we get some,
So bring it out here!

Repeat first verse

Joy to the World TRACK 2

First verse:
Joy to the world, the Lord is come!
Let earth receive her King;
Let ev'ry heart prepare Him room,
And heav'n and nature sing,
And heav'n and nature sing,
And heav'n, and heav'n and nature sing.

Second verse:
Joy to the world, the Savior reigns!
Let men their songs employ;
While fields and floods, rocks,
hills and plains
Repeat the sounding joy,
Repeat the sounding joy,
Repeat, repeat the sounding joy.

Third verse:
He rules the world with truth and grace,
And makes the nations prove
The glories of His righteousness,
And wonders of His love,
And wonders of His love,
And wonders, wonders of His love.

Angels We Have Heard on High TRACK 3

First verse:
Angels we have heard on high,
Sweetly singing o'er the plains;
And the mountains in reply,
Echoing their joyous strains.

Chorus:
Glo — ria,
In Excelsis Deo!
Glo — ria,
In Excelsis Deo!

Second verse:
Shepherd, why this jubilee?
Why your joyous strains prolong?
What the gladsome tidings be,
Which inspire your heavenly song?

Repeat chorus

Third verse:
Come to Bethlehem and see,
Him whose birth the angels sing.
Come adore on bended knee,
Christ the Lord, the newborn King.

Repeat chorus

Fourth verse:
See Him in a manger laid,
Whom the choirs of angels praise.
Mary, Joseph, lend your aid,
While our hearts in love we raise.

Repeat chorus

Deck the Halls TRACK 4

First verse:
Deck the halls with boughs of holly,
Fa la la la la, la la la la.
'Tis the season to be jolly,
Fa la la la la, la la la la.
Don we now our gay apparel,
Fa la la, la la la, la la la.
Troll the ancient Yuletide carol,
Fa la la la la, la la la la.

Second verse:
See the blazing Yule before us,
Fa la la la la, la la la la.
Strike the harp and join the chorus.
Fa la la la la, la la la la.
Follow me in merry measure,
Fa la la, la la la, la la la.
While I tell of Yuletide treasure,
Fa la la la la, la la la la.

Third verse:
Fast away the old year passes,
Fa la la la la, la la la la.
Hail the new, ye lads and lasses,
Fa la la la la, la la la la.
Sing we joyous, all together,
Fa la la, la la la, la la la.
Heedless of the wind and weather,
Fa la la la la, la la la la.

MUST BE SANTA   TRACK 5

First verse:
Who's got a beard that's long and white?
Santa's got a beard that's long and white!
Who comes around on a special night?
Santa comes around on a special night!
Special night, beard that's white—
Must be Santa,
Must be Santa,
Must be Santa, Santa Claus!

Second verse:
Who wears boots and a suit of red?
Santa wears boots and a suit of red!
Who wears a long cap on his head?
Santa wears a long cap on his head!
Cap on head, suit that's red—
Special night, beard that's white—
Must be Santa,
Must be Santa,
Must be Santa, Santa Claus!

Third verse:
Who's got a big red cherry nose?
Santa's got a big red cherry nose!
Who laughs this way: HO, HO, HO?
Santa laughs this way: HO, HO, HO!
HO HO HO, cherry nose—
Cap on head, suit that's red—
Special night, beard that's white—
Must be Santa,
Must be Santa,
Must be Santa, Santa Claus!

Fourth verse:
Who very soon will come our way?
Santa very soon will come our way!
Eight little reindeer pull his sleigh,
Santa's little reindeer pull his sleigh.
Reindeer sleigh, come our way—
HO, HO, HO, cherry nose—
Cap on head, suit that's red—
Special night, beard that's white—
Must be Santa,
Must be Santa,
Must be Santa, Santa Claus!

Good King Wenceslas TRACK 6

First verse:
Good King Wenceslas looked out
On the feast of Stephen.
When the snow lay round about
Deep and crisp and even.
Brightly shone the moon that night
Though the frost was cruel;
When a poor man came in sight
Gath'ring winter fuel.

Second verse:
"Hither, page, and stand by me
If thou know'st it, telling:
Yonder peasant, who is he?
Where and what his dwelling?"
"Sire, he lives a good league hence
Underneath the mountain.
Right against the forest fence
By Saint Agnes' fountain."

Third verse:
"Bring me flesh and bring me wine,
Bring me pine logs hither.
Thou and I will see him dine,
When we bear him thither."
Page and monarch forth they went,
Forth they went together.
Through the rude wind's wild lament
And the bitter weather.

Fourth verse:
"Sire, the night is darker now
And the wind blows stronger.
Fails my heart, I know not how,
I can go no longer."
"Mark my footsteps, my good page,
Tread thou in them boldly.
Thou shalt find the winter's rage
Freeze thy blood less coldly."

Fifth verse:
In his master's steps he trod,
Where the snow lay dinted.
Heat was in the very sod,
Which the Saint had printed.
Therefore, Christian men, be sure
Wealth or rank possessing.
Ye who now will bless the poor
Shall yourselves find blessing.

Go, Tell It On the Mountain TRACK 7

First verse:
While shepherds kept their watching,
Over silent flocks by night
Behold throughout the heavens,
There shone a holy light.

Refrain:
Go, tell it on the mountain,
Over the hills and everywhere;
Go, tell it on the mountain,
That Jesus Christ is born.

Second verse:
The shepherds feared and trembled,
When lo! above the earth
Rang out the angels' chorus
That hailed the Savior's birth.

Repeat refrain

Third verse:
Down in a lowly manger,
The humble Christ was born
And God sent us salvation,
That blessèd Christmas morn.

Repeat refrain

Fourth verse:
When I was a seeker,
I sought both night and day;
I sought the Lord to help me,
And he showed me the way.

Repeat refrain

Jingle Bells TRACK 8

First verse:
Dashing through the snow
In a one-horse open sleigh,
Over the fields we go,
Laughing all the way;
Bells on bob-tail ring,
Making spirits bright,
What fun it is to ride and sing
A sleighing song tonight!

Chorus:
Jingle bells, jingle bells,
Jingle all the way!
O what fun it is to ride
In a one-horse open sleigh!

Repeat

Second verse:
A day or two ago,

I thought I'd take a ride,
And soon Miss Fanny Bright
Was seated by my side;
The horse was lean and lank;
Misfortune seemed his lot;
He got into a drifted bank,
And we, we got upsot.

Repeat chorus

Third verse:
A day or two ago,
The story I must tell
I went out on the snow
And on my back I fell;
A gent was riding by
In a one-horse open sleigh,
He laughed as there
I sprawling lie,
But quickly drove away.

Repeat chorus

Fourth verse:
Now the ground is white
Go it while you're young,
Take the girls tonight
And sing this sleighing song;
Just get a bob-tailed bay
Two-forty as his speed
Hitch him to an open sleigh
And crack! you'll take the lead.

Repeat chorus

THE NIGHT BEFORE CHRISTMAS CAR-I-OKE TRACK 9

'Twas the night before Christmas,
    when all through the house
Not a creature was stirring,
    not even a mouse;
The stockings were hung
    by the chimney with care,
In hopes that St. Nicholas
    soon would be there;
The children were nestled
    all snug in their beds,
While visions of sugar-plums
    danced in their heads;
And mamma in her kerchief,
    and I in my cap,
Had just settled down
    for a long winter's nap.

Refrain:
Dasher, Dancer, Prancer, Vixen;
Comet, Cupid, Donner, Blitzen.

When out on the lawn
    there arose such a clatter,
I sprang from the bed to see
    what was the matter.

Away to the window I flew like a flash,
Tore open the shutters
and threw up the sash.
The moon on the breast
of the new-fallen snow
Gave the lustre of mid-day
to objects below,
When, what to my wondering eyes
should appear,
But a miniature sleigh,
and eight tiny reindeer.

Repeat refrain

With a little old driver, so lively and quick,
I knew in a moment it must be St. Nick.
More rapid than eagles
his coursers they came,
And he whistled, and shouted,
and called them by name;
"Now, Dasher! now, Dancer!
now, Prancer and Vixen!
On, Comet! on, Cupid!
on, Donner and Blitzen!
To the top of the porch!
to the top of the wall!
Now dash away! dash away! dash away all!"

Repeat refrain

As dry leaves that before
the wild hurricane fly,
When they meet with an obstacle,
mount to the sky,
So up to the house-top
the coursers they flew,
With the sleigh full of toys,
and St. Nicholas too.
And then, in a twinkling, I heard on the roof
The prancing and pawing of each little hoof.
As I drew in my hand,
and was turning around,
Down the chimney St. Nicholas
came with a bound.

Repeat refrain

He was dressed all in fur,
from his head to his foot,
And his clothes were all tarnished
with ashes and soot;
A bundle of toys he had flung on his back,
And he looked like a peddler
just opening his pack.
His eyes—how they twinkled!
His dimples, how merry!
His cheeks were like roses,
his nose like a cherry!
His droll little mouth was drawn up like a bow,
And the beard of his chin
was as white as the snow.

Repeat refrain

The stump of a pipe
he held tight in his teeth,
And the smoke it encircled
his head like a wreath;
He had a broad face and a little round belly,
That shook when he laughed,
like a bowlful of jelly.
He was chubby and plump,
a right jolly old elf,
And I laughed when I saw him,
in spite of myself;
A wink of his eye and a twist of his head,
Soon gave me to know
I had nothing to dread.

Repeat refrain

He spoke not a word,
but went straight to his work,
And filled all the stockings;
then turned with a jerk,
And laying his finger aside of his nose,
And giving a nod, up the chimney he rose;
He sprang to his sleigh,
to his team gave a whistle,
And away they all flew
like the down of a thistle.
But I heard him exclaim,
ere he drove out of sight,
"Happy Christmas to all,
and to all a good-night."

Repeat refrain

BAH, HUMBUG! TRACK 10

Words and music by David Schiller

First verse:

Mama said, no sneaking,
no peeking around the Christmas tree
Bah, humbug! Bah, humbug!
Papa said, got to get to bed early on
Christmas Eve
Bah, humbug! Bah, humbug!

Chorus:

Why, why, why must we go to bed?
We don't care what papa said,
We can't sleep!
We won't sleep!
We'll never sleep!
IT'S IMPOSSIBLE TO SLEEP!!!

Second verse:

Mama said, settle down now,
be good girls and boys,
Bah, humbug! Bah, humbug!
Papa said, I'm coming up
if I hear one more noise,
Bah, humbug! Bah, humbug!

Repeat chorus .

Bridge:
It's just so hard to wait for Christmas
The night drags on and on and on.
Here we go, tiptoe down the stairs
Plug in the tree, it shines so bright
Quiet now, the whole house is snoring
We're all along in the middle of the night
See the presents, piled like a mountain!
Boxes and boxes, all green and red
Pick one up, shake it and smell it—
HEY! PUT THAT DOWN! GET BACK TO BED!!!

Third verse:
Mama said, come here, kids, gather 'round
the Christmas tree
Merry Christmas, merry Christmas
Papa said, O why not,
here's a present to you from me,
Merry Christmas, merry Christmas!

Last chorus:
Boy, oh, boy, oh, what a Christmas Eve
Spent the night 'round
the Christmas tree
Now we got to sleep,
We really want to sleep,
Can we go to sleep?
WE NEED TO SLEEP!!!!

THE TWELVE DAYS OF CHRISTMAS TRACK 11

Day 1: A partridge in a pear tree
Day 2: Two turtle doves
Day 3: Three French hens
Day 4: Four calling birds
Day 5: Five golden rings
Day 6: Six geese a-laying
Day 7: Seven swans a-swimming
Day 8: Eight maids a-milking
Day 9: Nine ladies dancing
Day 10: Ten lords a-leaping
Day 11: Eleven pipers piping
Day 12: Twelve drummers drumming

The "O" Medley TRACK 15

O little town of Bethlehem,
How still we see thee lie!
Above thy deep and dreamless sleep
The silent stars go by.
Yet in thy dark streets shineth
The everlasting Light;
The hopes and fears of all the years
Are met in thee tonight.

O Holy night, the stars are brightly shining;
It is the night of the dear Savior's birth.
Long lay the world in sin and error pining,
Till He appeared and the soul felt His worth.
A thrill of hope, the weary world rejoices
For yonder breaks a new and glorious morn.
Fall on your knees! Oh, hear the angel voices!
O night divine! O night when Christ was born!
O night divine! O night when Christ was born.

O come, all ye faithful, joyful and triumphant,
O come ye, O come ye, to Bethlehem.
Come and behold Him,
born the King of angels;
O come, let us adore Him,
O come, let us adore Him,
O come, let us adore Him, Christ the Lord.

O Christmas tree! O Christmas tree!
Thy leaves are so unchanging;
O Christmas tree! O Christmas tree!
Thy leaves are so unchanging;
Not only green when summer's here,
But also when 'tis cold and drear.
O Christmas tree! O Christmas tree!
Thy leaves are so unchanging!

Silent Night TRACK 16

First verse:
Silent night, holy night!
All is calm, all is bright.
'Round yon virgin Mother and Child,
Holy infant so tender and mild.
Sleep in heavenly peace,
Sleep in heavenly peace.

Second verse:
Silent night, holy night!
Shepherds quake at the sight.
Glories stream from heaven afar.
Heav'nly hosts sing Alleluia;
Christ the Savior is born;
Christ the Savior is born.

Third verse:
Silent night, holy night!
Wondrous star, lend thy light!
With the angels, let us sing
Alleluia to our King!
Christ the Savior is here,
Jesus the Savior is here.

Fourth verse:
Silent night, holy night!
Son of God, love's pure light.
Radiant beams from Thy holy face,
With the dawn of redeeming grace.
Jesus, Lord, at Thy birth,
Jesus, Lord, at Thy birth.

THE HALLELUJAH CHORUS TRACK 17

Hallelujah hallelujah hallelujah
hallelujah hallelujah!
Hallelujah hallelujah hallelujah
hallelujah hallelujah!
For the Lord God omnipotent reigneth,
Hallelujah hallelujah hallelujah hallelujah!
For the Lord God omnipotent reigneth,
Hallelujah hallelujah hallelujah hallelujah!
For the Lord God omnipotent reigneth,
Hallelujah hallelujah hallelujah hallelujah!
Hallelujah hallelujah hallelujah hallelujah!
Hallelujah hallelujah hallelujah hallelujah!
(For the Lord God omnipotent reigneth)
Hallelujah hallelujah hallelujah hallelujah!
For the Lord God omnipotent reigneth!
(Hallelujah hallelujah hallelujah hallelujah)
Hallelujah!
The kingdom of this world
Is become the kingdom of our Lord,
And of His Christ, and of His Christ,
And He shall reign forever and ever,
And He shall reign forever and ever,
And He shall reign forever and ever,
And He shall reign forever and ever.
King of kings, forever and ever,
hallelujah, hallelujah!
And Lord of lords, forever and ever,
hallelujah hallelujah!
King of kings, forever and ever,
hallelujah, hallelujah!
And Lord of lords, forever and ever,
hallelujah hallelujah!
King of kings, forever and ever,
hallelujah, hallelujah!
And Lord of lords—
King of kings and Lord of lords—
And He shall reign,
And He shall reign,
And He shall reign,
He shall reign,

And He shall reign forever and ever!
King of kings forever and ever—
And Lord of lords hallelujah hallelujah
And He shall reign forever and ever—
King of kings and Lord of lords,
King of kings and Lord of lords,
And He shall reign forever and ever—
Forever and ever and ever and ever,
(King of kings and Lord of lords)
Hallelujah hallelujah hallelujah hallelujah!
Hallelujah!

Auld Lang Syne TRACK 18

First verse:
Should auld acquaintance be forgot,
And never brought to mind?
Should auld acquaintance be forgot,
And days o' lang syne!

Chorus:
For auld lang syne, my dear
For auld lang syne,
We'll tak a cup o' kindness yet,
For auld lang syne!

Second verse:
We twa hae run about the braes,
And pu'd the gowans fine,
But we've wander'd mony a weary foot
Sin' auld lang syne.

Third verse:
We twa hae paidl't in the burn
Frae morning sun till dine,
But seas between us braid hae roar'd
Sin' auld lang syne.

Fourth verse:
And there's a hand, my trusty fiere,
And gie's a hand o' thine,
And we'll tak a right guid willie-waught
For auld lang syne!

Fifth verse:
And surely ye'll be your pint' stoup,
And surely I'll be mine!
And we'll tak a cup o' kindness yet
For auld lang syne!

Bonus Tracks

O Little Town of Bethlehem TRACK 19

First verse:
O little town of Bethlehem,
How still we see thee lie!
Above thy deep and dreamless sleep,
The silent stars go by.
Yet in thy dark streets shineth
The everlasting Light;
The hopes and fears of all the years
Are met in thee tonight.

Second verse:
For Christ is born of Mary,
And gathered all above,
While mortals sleep, the angels keep
Their watch of wondering love.
O morning stars, together
Proclaim the holy birth,
And praises sing to God the King,
And peace to men on earth!

Third verse:
How silently, how silently,
The wondrous Gift is giv'n;
So God imparts to human hearts
The blessings of His Heav'n.
No ear may hear His coming,
But in this world of sin,
Where meek souls will receive Him still,
The dear Christ enters in.

Fourth verse:
Where children pure and happy
Pray to the blessèd Child,
Where misery cries out to Thee,
Son of the mother mild;
Where charity stands watching
And faith holds wide the door,
The dark night wakes, the glory breaks,
And Christmas comes once more.

O Holy Night TRACK 20

First verse:
O Holy night, the stars are brightly shining
It is the night of the dear Savior's birth.
Long lay the world in sin and error pining
Till He appeared and the soul felt His worth.
A thrill of hope, the weary world rejoices
For yonder breaks a new and glorious morn.

Refrain:
Fall on your knees! Oh, hear the angel voices!

O night divine! O night when Christ was born!
O night divine! O night, O night divine!

Second verse:
Led by the light of faith serenely beaming
With glowing hearts by His cradle we stand.
So led by light of a star sweetly gleaming
Here came the wise men from the Orient land.
The King of Kings lay in lowly manger
In all our trials born to be our friend.

Repeat refrain

Third verse:
Truly He taught us to love one another
His law is love and His gospel is peace.
Chains shall He break,
for the slave is our brother
And in His name all oppression shall cease.
Sweet hymns of joy in grateful chorus rise we
Let all within us praise His holy name.

Repeat refrain

O Come, All Ye Faithful TRACK 21

First verse:
O come, all ye faithful, joyful and triumphant,
O come ye, O come ye to Bethlehem.
Come and behold Him,
born the King of angels.

Refrain:
O come, let us adore Him,
O come, let us adore Him,
O come, let us adore Him, Christ the Lord.

Second verse:
Sing, choirs of angels, sing in exultation;
O sing, all ye citizens of heaven above!
Glory to God, all glory in the highest.

Repeat refrain

Third verse:
See how the shepherds,
summoned to His cradle,
Leaving their flocks, draw nigh to gaze;
We too will thither bend our joyful footsteps.

Repeat refrain

O CHRISTMAS TREE TRACK 22

First verse:

O Christmas tree! O Christmas tree!
Thy leaves are so unchanging.
O Christmas tree! O Christmas tree!
Thy leaves are so unchanging.
Not only green when summer's here,
But also when 'tis cold and drear.
O Christmas tree! O Christmas tree!
Thy leaves are so unchanging.

Second verse:

O Christmas tree! O Christmas tree!
Much pleasure thou can'st give me.
O Christmas tree! O Christmas tree!
Much pleasure thou can'st give me.
How often has the Christmas tree
Afforded me the greatest glee.
O Christmas tree! O Christmas tree!
Much pleasure thou can'st give me.

Third verse:

O Christmas tree! O Christmas tree!
Thy candles shine so brightly.
O Christmas tree! O Christmas tree!
Thy candles shine so brightly.
From base to summit, gay and bright,
There's only splendor for the sight.
O Christmas tree! O Christmas tree!
Thy candles shine so brightly.

German verse:

O Tannenbaum, O Tannenbaum,
Wie treu sind deine Blätter!
O Tannenbaum, O Tannenbaum,
Wie treu sind deine Blätter!
Du grünst nicht nur zur Sommerzeit,
Nein auch im Winter, wenn es schneit.
O Tannenbaum, O Tannenbaum,
Wie treu sind deine Blätter!